A Little Book of Drugs

Activities to explore drug issues with young people

Vanessa Rogers

Published by

The National Youth Agency

Eastgate House,
19-23 Humberstone Road,
Leicester LE5 3GJ
Tel: 0116 242 7350.
Fax: 0116 242 7444.
E-mail: nya@nya.org.uk
Website: www.nya.org.uk

ISBN: 0 86155 330 6

© June 2006

Price: £8.50

Individual activities can be photocopied free of
charge for non-commercial educational purposes.

Design: Sanjay Kukadia
Printed in the UK by Joseph Ball, Leicester.

Contents

ACKNOWLEDGMENTS

Dave Price (A-DASH), Chrysalis Drugs Project, Hertfordshire Young People's Substance Misuse Team, Joanna Howlett (Hertfordshire Connexions Service), Gillian Porter (QE11), Deborah Mulroney (HCC School Improvement and Development Service), Joshua, Toby and Sophie Oakes-Rogers (Simon Balle School). Thanks also to my team and any other youth workers or personal advisers not mentioned who have been a part of the projects mentioned.

ABOUT THE AUTHOR

Vanessa Rogers is a qualified teacher and youth worker with a masters degree in Community Education and over ten years experience within Hertfordshire Youth Service both at practitioner and management levels. She has gained extensive experience managing a large youth centre, developing detached projects and working directly with young people in urban and rural areas. Currently employed by Hertfordshire County Council Children, Schools and Family Service, Vanessa manages a multi-agency Specialist Adolescent Team developing creative strategies to engage with young people at risk.

This title is part of a series of seven pocket resource books; 'Teambuilding', 'The Good Games Book', 'Icebreakers', 'Evaluations and Endings', 'Act Out!' a collection of drama based activities and A Little Book of Alcohol.

There is also series of social education handbooks written by Vanessa for youth workers, YOT workers, Connexions Personal Advisers and also for teachers delivering PSHE and Citizenship programmes in schools within the National Curriculum framework. "Have you ever....?" (A resource handbook for detached workers); "Let's Talk Relationships..."; "So you want to work with Young People?" ;(A resource for training and supporting volunteer workers); "Exploring Feelings" (for work with young people under 14) "Art Unlimited" (ideas to engage young people in creative projects); "All the Right Connections" (for supporting personal advisers in their work with young people); "Work with Young Men" a collection of activities to support and motivate young men; "Young People and Citizenship" and the most recent title "Work with Young Women".

All titles are published by and available from The National Youth Agency. For more details about books or training click onto www.nya.org.uk. Alternatively go to www. resourceplanet.com, the website for Vanessa Rogers, to contact the author or find out about training events.

INTRODUCTION

This resource is a diverse collection of activities suitable for work with young people aged 13 to 16 to look at issues around substance misuse. It also includes information to support you and signposts to other agencies for more specialist intervention.

Warm ups

This section offers short activities and exercises to open a session around drugs or to re-energise a group after a discussion. Easy to use, these are ideas to introduce issues and enable you to begin to assess the level of knowledge and attitudes to drugs within the group.

Activities

Including ideas for group and individual work these activities look at three main areas:

*   Information and knowledge about drug issues.
*   Exploring attitudes and values, including peer influence and reducing risk.
*   Developing skills to make healthy choices.

Reviewing

The final pages suggest a few ideas for reviewing and reinforcing learning.

DRUG INFORMATION

Most young people will come into contact with drugs, tobacco or alcohol at some stage in their life and will need to make decisions and choices. The aim of drug awareness work is to give information and support that enables young people to develop skills that help them towards making positive choices and keeping safe.

Research undertaken by the Department for Education and Skills in 2000 reports that young people see effective drug education as "honest, age appropriate and not simply advice not to take drugs" . Therefore, drugs awareness sessions must be relevant to the lives of young people and reflect their own knowledge and experiences of drugs, both positive and negative.

Sessions and activities must be factually correct and offered in a non-judgmental way to encourage young people to question their existing attitudes and values and think through the possible consequences of actions and choices. This includes giving information about the legal status of drugs and the consequences of illegal drug use.

As well as giving information about the immediate and possible long term health effects of substance misuse it is vital that young people understand that the effects of drugs can be unpredictable. Street drugs don't come with a label on the side (and even drugs that do are not always 100 per cent safe) to tell you what is in them and the effect can vary from person to person.

[1] Drug education in school – what pupils think 7/11/01 www.dfes.gov.uk

This is not just dependent on the purity of the drug but also the strength of the dose, whether it is mixed with other drugs, where the young person is when they take the drug, who they are with and most importantly how they are feeling before they take any substance that alters the way their mind or body works.

This includes those "hard to reach" young people and young people with disabilities who need specific skills and innovative ways of engaging them.

1. PARENTS AND CARERS

Many parents and carers feel very uncomfortable discussing drug and alcohol issues with their young people. Parents need to feel informed about the drug education their young people are participating in and confident that their own knowledge, values and cultures are respected.

Parents also need to be clear about youth club or school procedures and policy if a young person is involved in a drug-related incident, ranging from smoking in a non-smoking area to the possession or dealing of illegal substances. This is particularly important in any situation where a worker is in loco parentis, for example on a residential. Information you may want to give parents should include the worker's legal requirements, other agencies that may be informed and any club bans or exclusion processes that may be enforced, including the right to appeal.

As well as handing out consent forms prior to the drug education programme, you may also want to send home a leaflet, or direct parents/carers to the Talk to Frank website (www.talktofrank.com) which has lots of facts about drugs and leaflets available free of charge.

2. THE MISUSE OF DRUGS ACT

The Misuse of Drugs Act (1971) divides drugs into three classes as follows:

Class A:
These include cocaine and crack (a form of cocaine), ecstasy, heroin, LSD, methadone, magic mushrooms and any Class B drug which is prepared for injection.

Maximum Penalties
Possession – seven years + fine
Supply – Life + fine

Class B:
These include amphetamines and barbiturates.
Maximum Penalties
Possession – Five years + fine
Supply – 14 years + fine

Class C:
These include cannabis, GHB, Rohypnol and minor tranquillisers such as Valium.
Maximum Penalties
Possession – Two years + fine
Supply – 14 years + fine

Offences under the Misuse of Drugs Act can include:

• Possession of a controlled drug.
• Possession with intent to supply another person.
• Production, cultivation or manufacture of controlled drugs.
• Supplying another person with a controlled drug.
• Offering to supply another person with a controlled drug.

• Import or export of controlled drugs.
• Allowing premises you occupy or manage to be used for the consumption of certain controlled drugs or supply or production of any controlled drug.

WARM UPS

3. DEFINITIONS

This is a whole group warm up activity that encourages young people to share their understanding and knowledge.

Aim

To reinforce the wide spectrum of substances meant by the term 'drugs', both legal and illegal.

You will need
• Flipchart and markers

How to do it

Start off by asking the group to idea storm the names of as many drugs as they can think of. Stress you are not asking how many they have taken or seen, just heard of.

Record them onto flipchart paper as the young people call them out.

Next ask the young people to split into groups of three or four. Their challenge is to come up with a definition of what a 'drug' is. They can illustrate this if they want to – the point is to discuss the term and reach agreement.

Once everyone has finished invite each group to share what they have been working on.

Finally offer this definition;

"A drug is a substance that changes the way the body or mind works" (DfES 2003)

What do the young people think of this?

Explain that this is a definition that schools and other professionals work to.

Display the young people's definitions on the wall to refer to in future sessions.

4. STEREOTYPES

This activity explores stereotypes and is good to use as a warm up with small groups of young people.

Aim

To raise awareness of stereotyping and encourage further discussions.

You will need

- Flipchart paper
- Plenty of coloured markers
- Blutack

How to do it

Hand each young person a piece of flip chart paper and some markers. Explain that you are going to give a description of a person and you want them to draw the first things that come into their head. Emphasise that this is not a drawing competition and that they can use any style that they like.

When everyone is settled with pen poised say "DRUG DEALER"!

Give the group ten minutes to draw on their flipchart sheets, encouraging them to think about age, gender, ethnicity and where they might expect to find the dealer, as well as clothes and hairstyles. Ask that they do this without looking at each others' sheets for the moment.

At the end of the time ask the young people to stop and gather together with their pictures.

Ask each young person to show their picture to the rest of the group, explaining any particular bits they want to draw attention to and then blutack them up onto the wall.

Invite the young people to ask questions of each other about what they have drawn.

When all the pictures are on display go back and review the "gallery". Are the drug dealers all shown as women? All men? What other similarities are there? Are they young or old? Encourage the group to discuss how they decided what to draw and what influenced their choices.

Pull together any main themes emerging from the group and cluster them onto another flipchart sheet. Facilitate a group discussion about what has been written to look at any stereotypes emerging. How true are these? Ask the young people to think about their own experiences or knowledge and compare this with the list the group came up with.

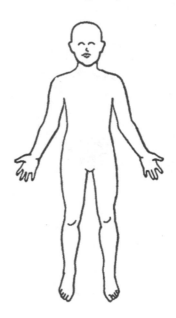

The National Youth Agency

5. DRUG PAIRS

This is a good warm up to divide the group into pairs.

Aim

To introduce the session and provide opportunities for the group to interact as they find their "pair".

You will need

• A set of the drug pairs cards
• A few spare cards in case you have too many young people and have to improvise

How to do it

Shuffle the cards and ask each young person to choose one. If you have an odd number in the group use one of the blanks to make up another card along one of the themes, for example "ECSTASY", "PILLS" & "Es".

Invite everyone to look at their card, but ask them not to tell anybody else what is written on it. It does not matter if you have duplicate "pairs", so long as each person can find a partner.

Ask the group to go off and "find" their pair. They can only do this by asking questions about the drug on their card; for example they cannot ask, "Have you a got a card with another name for Ecstasy on it?" but could ask, "Are you a Class A drug?"

Once everyone has found the card that corresponds to their own explain that their "pair" will now be their partner for the next activity.

DRUG PAIRS

CANNABIS	LSD	COCAINE	SOLVENTS	CRACK
GRASS	ACID	COKE	GLUE	ROCK
ECSTASY	HEROIN	TOBACCO	AMPHETAMINE	MAGIC MUSHROOMS
PILLS	SMACK	FAGS	SPEED	MAGICS

6. DESCRIBE IT!
This is an exercise to demonstrate the importance of effective listening in communication.

Aim
To guess your partner's drug card from the information they give you.

You will need
- Copies of the Drug Cards (you will need a card for each young person)

How to do it
Divide the group in half, one half will be 'As' for this activity and the other 'Bs'. Ask the 'Bs' to go and find an 'A' to work with so that they are in pairs. Next ask each pair to take two chairs, place them back to back and then sit down so that they are facing away from each other.

Hand all the 'As' a drug card, and ask them not to show their partner, explaining that the 'Bs' task in this first round is to listen as carefully as possible to the information that will be given to them. The 'As' should then proceed to describe the drug on their card as carefully and in as much detail as possible, giving all the information that they know or have heard about it. The only rule is that they cannot actually say the name!

After about two minutes call time and invite the 'Bs' to guess what was on the card.

Collect in and shuffle before handing out to the 'Bs' for another round.

Review the exercise – what made it easy
to know what was on the card? What made
it hard? What information was the most
useful?

DRUG CARDS

CANNABIS	TOBACCO	COCAINE
ECSTASY	HEROIN	CRACK
SKUNK	LSD	AMPHETAMINES
STEROIDS	CAFFEINE	ALCOHOL

7. I HEARD

This is another small group activity that explores myths and stereotypes based on information that young people may have heard about drugs.

Aim
To promote discussion and explore young people's knowledge.

You will need
- A copy of the 'I Heard' sheet for each young person cut up into strips
- An envelope for each set
- Pens
- A box

How to do it
Hand each young person an envelope containing a set of the 'I Heard' slips and a pen. Ask them to quickly complete the sentence on each piece of paper. Encourage them to go with their first thoughts rather than deliberating too long.

When they have completed all their slips collect them all in the box. Make sure you shake the box well so that all the statements become muddled up.

Now ask the young people to sit in a circle and pass the box around the circle. Each young person should take out a slip and read it out.

For each one ask them to consider if they think the statement is true and where they think the ideas came from. Once the person who has read it out has spoken encourage comments from the rest of the group.

Reinforce correct information shared and facilitate a discussion around stereotypes and values around drugs information.

I HEARD

All drugs are ...	Using cannabis leads to ...
People take drugs because ...	All drug addicts are ...
Drugs you buy over the counter are ...	Drug dealers are ...
If you try drugs ...	If the police catch you with drugs ...

The National Youth Agency

8. DRUGS WORDSEARCH
This warm up uses a format that most young people will know so it requires little explanation!

Aim
To open up discussions around drugs and substance misuse and encourage young people to work together

You will need
- Copies of the wordsearch enlarged to A3 size and coloured felt pens
- Prize (optional!)

How to do it
Divide the young people into groups of three and hand each group an A3 copy of the wordsearch and a coloured felt pen.

Explain that the task is to complete the wordsearch as quickly as possible. First group finished wins!

Review the activity making sure that young people are clear about the meaning of terms used and explaining if they aren't.

DRUGS WORDSEARCH

C	W	D	V	J	U	E	N	I	A	C	O	C	O
A	S	O	L	V	E	Y	J	M	S	S	A	L	L
N	O	I	T	P	I	R	C	S	E	R	P	A	M
N	L	E	E	I	D	F	T	P	C	O	O	S	J
A	V	S	G	L	J	K	M	S	S	X	A	S	G
B	E	Q	A	L	H	E	E	T	T	K	V	I	S
I	N	D	E	P	R	E	S	S	A	N	T	F	M
S	T	R	V	G	E	R	T	R	S	U	K	I	O
A	S	U	G	Y	U	R	I	Y	Y	K	V	C	K
I	S	G	Q	A	A	M	M	U	O	S	C	A	E
N	C	B	U	N	J	K	U	I	I	T	S	T	W
J	W	T	L	A	G	E	L	L	I	R	E	I	A
E	S	J	A	G	E	R	A	L	V	E	T	O	N
C	D	B	L	O	O	E	N	R	D	E	G	N	J
T	B	L	O	O	D	S	T	R	E	A	M	F	B
H	A	L	L	U	C	I	N	O	G	E	N	I	C

Search to find the following substance related words

Cannabis	Hallucinogenic
Stimulant	Drug
Classification	Solvents
Depressant	Cocaine
Prescription	Skunk
Illegal	Pill
Bloodstream	Smoke
Ecstasy	Inject

9. WORD SCRAMBLE
This activity is another one that will be familiar to young people so should need little explanation.

Aim
To focus on drug terms and familiarise young people with them.

You will need
• Copies of the 'Scramble Words' sheet
• Pens

How to do it
Ask the young people to choose a partner to work with.

Hand out a copy of the 'Scramble Words' sheet to each couple and a pen. Explain that the task is to unscramble the words, using the clues to help them, as fast as they can.

First pair to complete the sheet wins!

Here are the answers for when you need them.
Cocaine
Amphetamine
Aspirin
Cannabis
Heroin
Solvents
Ketamine
Tobacco
Poppers
Ecstasy

WORD SCRAMBLE SHEET

oceinca – A white powder derived from the coca plant =	**etsslnov** – These substances are inhaled =
eitahemanpm – A stimulant drug =	**mteeakni** – An anaesthetic drug legally produced for use in human and animal medicine =
pinrisa – A well known painkiller =	**cotoacb** – This contains the stimulant drug nicotine =
scibanan – This substance is usually smoked =	**rpeppso** – A term for amyl, butyl or isobutyl nitrates =
irohne – A painkilling drug made from the opium poppy =	**ssyetac** – The chemical name for this is Methylendioxymethylamphetamine or MDMA =

10. PROBLEMS AND BENEFITS

This warm up reinforces that not all drugs are 'bad' all of the time.

Aim

To look at the positive use of drugs and medicines as well as identifying drug related issues.

You will need

• Nothing

How to do it

This is a circle activity so invite the young people to sit down in a large circle.

Explain that you want each young person to in turn suggest a 'problem' that they think drugs can bring and a 'benefit' that they think drugs have. If you think that the group may be reluctant then make a suggestion yourself first to get them started.

Once everyone has shared their ideas pull out and discuss points making sure that you challenge any incorrect statements and reinforce good points.

Finally reinforce the important role that drugs have played in the fight against disease and illness.

11. DRUGS IN SPORT

This is a quick warm up to open up discussion around drugs in sport. It works well with the activities in the next section.

Aim

To quickly assess opinion in the group and get an understanding of existing knowledge.

You will need

- A red, yellow and green card for each person
- A copy of the drugs in sports warm up sheet

How to do it

Give each young person a red, yellow and a green card. Explain that you are going to read a series of statements and you want the young people to raise the card that corresponds with their opinion.

RED = No, I disagree!
YELLOW = I want to say something about this
GREEN = Yes, I agree!

Allow time for people to ask questions or make comments about the statements. If no one uses a yellow card you can ask questions or challenge red and green cards yourself.

Highlight group agreement and where people feel most different.

The National Youth Agency

DRUGS IN SPORT

1. Random drugs tests are the only way to stop athletes cheating.

2. Drugs in sport have only been a problem since the 1980s

3. Athletes caught using steroids should be barred for life from competing.

4. Disabled athletes should be subject to the same rules as other athletes otherwise it isn't fair.

5. If someone refuses a drugs test then he/she must have something to hide.

6. It would be better if every sportsperson was drugs tested before competing.

7. I think sportspeople provide good role models for young people.

8. If a sportsperson is found to have used drugs before winning a medal then it should be taken from them.

9. Athletes who are wrongly convicted should be given their titles back and apologised to.

10. Some over the counter remedies for colds and flu contain banned drugs that can make athletes test positive for drugs.

ACTIVITIES

12. INFORMATION EXERCISE
This is an activity which will help you assess the preferred learning styles within the group.

Aim
To encourage young people to think about the ways that they learn about drugs best.

You will need
- Six x pieces of flipchart paper
- Blutack
- Pictures (optional)
- Six x different colour packs of Post it notes

How to do it
In advance take the pieces of flipchart paper and label them 'FRIENDS', 'ADULT YOU LIVE WITH', 'YOUTH WORKER', 'LEAFLETS' & 'IT'. To make these more visual either draw simple pictures such as a phone with text messages showing or a computer screen on the IT sheet, or cut out pictures to stick on.

Divide up the Post it notes so that each member of the group will have a small wad with one of each colour in it. Choose which colours you want to represent the numbers one to six.

When the young people arrive start off by explaining that we all learn about things in lots of different ways. This includes information about drugs that is available from a wide range of reliable and not so reliable sources. Encourage a quick idea storm to get ideas from the young people about where they get knowledge about drugs from and the reliability of it.

Next stick the posters with the six different ways of obtaining information up around the wall and hand each young person a stack of Post it notes.

Invite the young people to think about the method they like best and to go and stick the colour that you have designated onto that sheet. Repeat the exercise in order of preference until they have used all the notes.

Review the results and discuss with the group the top choices, asking the reasons why they like this method of communication and why others are less successful for them.

13. WORD SCATTER
This is an activity to work around attitudes and values.

Aim
To look at language and attitudes associated with substance use/misuse.

You will need
- Post it notes
- Large sheets of paper
- Felt tip pens

How to do it
Divide the young people into groups of four. Hand out a small wad of Post it notes and a pen to each young person and a large sheet of paper to each group. Working in their groups invite each young person to think of as many words or thoughts that come into their head when they hear the term 'substance misuse', write them on a Post it note and stick it onto their group sheet. If you think the group will be unfamiliar with this term just use the word 'drug user'. At this stage all contributions are welcomed and not challenged.

After five minutes call time and ask each group to display their sheet to share with the whole group. Often the list of words will include a number of slang words or emotive terms that may be considered offensive, such as druggy, smack head, addict etc. Ask the young people if they have used words like these. What feelings are generated in the person who uses these words: fear, condemnation, superiority?

Explore with the group some of these terms and the possible effect upon our attitudes around substance misuse. Where do we get our information from? Is it true of all people who misuse substances? Does it differ for legal and illegal drugs?

Misuse

Drug User

druggy

Fear

Substance

Condemnation

addict

illegal

Superiority

14. ACCEPTABLE/UNACCEPTABLE
The idea of this activity is to get young people to think about their own values and those of their peers.

Aim
The aim of the session is to open up a discussion around personal values.

You will need
- A set of the cards depicting situations
- A card marked "acceptable" and a card marked "unacceptable"

How to do it
Hand each young person a situation card and ask them to read it, but not show anyone else.

Mark two opposing poles on the floor with the "acceptable" and "unacceptable" cards. Explain that what you want the young people to do is to "rate" the cards as acceptable or unacceptable behaviour. Stress that there is not always a right or wrong answer, although there are legal implications for some choices. Some responses are based on cultural or social acceptance, which may differ within the group.

For each card agreement needs to be reached within the group before it is placed in a zone. If there are different views, facilitate a discussion ensuring that everyone is heard and more assertive members of the group do not try and take over.

When all the cards are placed down review the process. How easy was it to reach consensus? Was it easy to listen to views that opposed their own? What influenced their decisions?

ACCEPTABLE/UNACCEPTABLE CARDS

Giving a friend a painkiller if they have a headache	An athlete taking steroids to improve their performance
A man ordering Viagra from the internet to improve his sexual performance	Putting a substance in someone's drink without them knowing
Taking sleeping tablets prescribed for someone else as you are having difficulties getting to sleep	Smoking cannabis to help you relax
Buying cigarettes for someone you know is under 16	Driving a car after drinking alcohol
Clubbing together with mates to buy a gram of cocaine before a party	Calling someone 'mad' because they are prescribed anti-depressive drugs

Putting pressure on someone to have sex when they have taken Ecstasy	Excusing aggressive behaviour by saying that it was caused by alcohol
Being unable to remember what happened the night before after taking strong prescription only painkillers with alcohol	Not being motivated to get up and go to school the morning after smoking skunk
Buying someone a double shot of spirits when they asked for a single	Selling solvents to younger people that you suspect may misuse them
Reassuring a friend who regularly smokes cannabis whilst they are feeling paranoid and anxious	Calling a friend's parents because they are unconscious after drinking a bottle of spirits

15. SMOKING BOTTLE

This is a good small group activity to use as part of a health session around smoking and the effects it has on the body. It may be a good idea to check out with the group who is a regular smoker or has parents/carers who smoke at home so that you can signpost them to further support if appropriate.

Aim

To demonstrate how tar collects in the lungs when nicotine is inhaled, using a smoking bottle.

You will need

- a filter cigarette
- plasticine or Blutack
- cotton wool
- a large empty, clean, dry, clear plastic bottle
- matches
- leaflets for support groups/giving up information

How to do it

1. Before the group arrives, set up your smoking bottle. You do this by taking the empty bottle and pushing cotton wool into the neck until you have a good size wad covering the bottom of the bottle. Next take the cigarette and place it into the neck holding it in place with some plasticine or Blutack.

2. Open by explaining that the aim of the session is to look at smoking, in particular cigarettes, and the effect it can have on

your health. You may want to facilitate a short discussion or conduct a quick poll to see how many of the young people smoke or have ever tried a cigarette. Refer to your group contract and the confidentiality rule that was agreed.

3. Bring out the smoking bottle and ask for a volunteer.

4. Invite the volunteer to light the cigarette in the top of the bottle. Once it is alight ask the young person to squeeze the sides of the bottle gently to simulate inhaling and exhaling.

5. Pass the bottle around the group inviting everyone to have a go.

6. As the bottle is passed ask the group to comment on any changes they see to the cotton wool. It will gradually turn brown as the tar is collected.

7. Review what has happened and ask the group to consider the effects smoking has on a person's lungs based on their findings.

8. Answer any questions that arise, hand out leaflets and ensure that the young people know where they can go for further help or support if necessary.

9. Identify any further smoking related issues the group would like to explore in follow up sessions.

16. WHAT HAPPENS NEXT?

This is shown as a small group activity but if you have a very small group give each young person a scenario to work with.

Aim

To encourage young people to think through possible consequences of substance related situations.

You will need

- A flipchart sheet for each group
- Pens

How to do it

Divide the large group into smaller groups of three or four. Hand each group a different scenario explaining that each depicts a situation where drugs or alcohol is an issue.

Give each group a flipchart sheet and markers and ask them to construct a comic strip to show what happens next. Encourage the groups to think about the consequences of actions, what they may have done differently in the situation and what could be done to resolve the scenario.

1	A 14-year-old young man is caught at school with cannabis in his school bag
2	A 21-year-old young man offers an 'E' to a 15-year-old young woman he has just met in a club
3	A 17-year-old young woman passes out at a club after drinking a bottle of vodka
4	A 16-year-old student tells her tutor that she uses cannabis to relax her

17. DRUGS JENGA

This activity uses a well-known game and adapts it to look at drugs issues. The fact that the questions are random means that it is possible to discuss attitudes, knowledge and assess skills in a non-personal way.

Aim

To remove wooden bricks from the Jenga tower and answer questions

You will need

- One wooden Jenga game (a Milton Bradley game) on which you have written the drugs questions
- Black permanent marker pen
- A flat, level surface

How to do it

To create the game:

Write with a black permanent marker on random Jenga blocks the name of a drug or a question from the list on the next page. You can add your own to meet the needs of the young people playing. The questions will help open up discussions around attitudes to drug taking in the group and check out skills.

To play the game:

Build the Jenga blocks into a high tower. Each player in turn, including the youth workers, removes one block from the stack of Jenga blocks without knocking the whole thing over. If it has a question on then the young person should read it out loud and answer and then replace the block at the top of the tower. If they pull out the name of a drug the task is to tell the group three things they know about that drug and then put the block back on top. If a blank block is pulled out then it should just be placed back on the top of the tower.

If a player is uncomfortable about answering any question, they can put the block on top without answering, but must then take another block.

If a block is pulled that has already been answered, then the young person must also pull another one.

If a player knocks the whole thing over, the game is finished and all the other players get to choose any of the questions to ask

before re-building the tower and starting again.

DRUGS JENGA - QUESTIONS AND NAMES

COCAINE	CANNABIS	ECSTASY
SKUNK	MAGIC MUSHROOMS	CRACK
HEROIN	SOLVENTS	LSD
AMPHETAMINE	POPPERS	TRANQUILLISERS
What are some of the health risks for injecting drugs?	If a friend collapses after using drugs what should you do?	Why do you think it can be dangerous to mix drugs?
What can you do to prevent your drink being 'spiked' in a pub or club?	What class of drug is cannabis?	Which common drinks contain the stimulant caffeine?
Name some of the solvents that can be found in most homes?	Why is dehydration a problem for ecstasy users?	What are the dangers of using solvents alone?

The National Youth Agency

Do you think there is a link between drug use and unsafe sex? Why?	Who could you tell if you were worried about a friend's drug use?	What should you do if you find used needles and syringes in a park or playground?
What are the dangers of exceeding the dosage of paracetemol?	Name three illegal substances.	Someone offers you a lift home, but you know they have been smoking puff – what do you do?
What is the difference between cocaine and crack?	What would you tell a friend who wants to try ecstasy for the first time?	What is the difference between cannabis and skunk?
What are the names of some commonly prescribed tranquillisers?	What does LSD usually look like?	Do you think most young people try illegal drugs at some point?
Tell us some of the street names used for cannabis.	What is cocaine often called?	What could you do if someone offered you a drug and you didn't want to try it?

18. EXPLORING ATTITUDES

This is an activity that is played like a game but does challenge some basic attitudes in a non-confrontational way encouraging group members to communicate what they really think.

Aim

To explore young people's attitude to drugs and the surrounding issues. It also encourages young people to consider legal drugs such as alcohol and cigarettes as well.

You will need

- Leaflets and information that answer some of the questions that may be raised.

How to do it

Explain to the group that you are going to read out a series of statements that describe feelings and views around drug and alcohol issues. The area to the left of you is the "agree" zone, to the right is a "disagree" zone and in the middle is the "undecided" zone.

Ask the young people to show you how they feel about the statement you read out by moving to the zone that most reflects their opinion. Try and encourage the young people to make their own decisions, rather than following their friends' views.

Leave space between statements to review what the group are saying and make sure that there is an opportunity for the young

people to ask questions and debate any issues raised.

Agree with the group any follow up work or future sessions to take this further.

STATEMENTS

1. All young people try drugs

2. People who get cancer through smoking should have to wait for hospital treatment as it is their own fault

3. If you start smoking cannabis it always leads to hard drugs

4. Celebrities should set a good example to young people and not use drugs

5. It is a sign of maturity to be able to hold your drink

6. It is safe to use someone else's prescription drugs if you have the same symptoms

7. Cocaine is a drug for the rich and famous

8. It is okay to smoke as long as you give up before you are 30

9. The media portray all drug users as criminals and addicts

10. If you are caught with drugs you should be sent to prison

11. It is okay to use drugs at weekends, as long as you don't do it every night you will not damage your health

12. All drugs should be legalised and taxed by the government

13. Heroin is an older person's drug

14. If the government puts up the price of cigarettes enough no one will smoke

15. You can always tell if someone is a drug addict

16. Most drug users become criminals to pay for their habit

17. What is safe drug use for one person may not be for another

18. Smoking helps to keep your weight down

19. LEGAL DRUGS GAME

This is an activity for younger groups or young people with disabilities that assesses base knowledge. You can make a new set of cards to represent illegal drugs or introduce different categories later on.

Aim

To clarify the level of knowledge in the group and the fact that not all drugs are illegal or "bad".

You will need

• A set of cards for each group
• Leaflets and drug information to support the session

How to do it

1. Point out that not all drugs are illegal. Introduce the idea of legal drugs, some of which are used everyday, such as caffeine in drinks, and others found at home in the form of household cleaners etc. A good way of introducing the topic of medicines is to say that all medicines are drugs, but not all drugs are medicine and discuss who should administer common medicines and the dangers of self-administration. If you are working with young people who regularly use prescribed drugs, then discuss the importance of never giving medicine prescribed for you to anyone else. Check out the young people's knowledge of the terms used.

2. Divide large group into smaller groups of five or six.

3. Hand each group a set of cards in an envelope and a sheet of large paper divided into five sections "SOLVENTS", "CAFFEINE", "MEDICINES", "ALCOHOL" and "TOBACCO"

4. Allow 15 to 20 minutes for each group to talk about each slip and place it in the correct place.

5. Check out placement and correct if wrong.

6. Give each group a category to work further on, handing out the leaflets for reference and set them the task of

- naming two other drugs that could be in that category;
- describing the effect of the drug; and
- describing a danger of using the drug.

If this is not appropriate due to the level of understanding in the group, do the first part and then discuss when they might see people using the drug – for example alcohol at a wedding, or paracetamol if you have a headache. You can then go through the dangers of misusing the drug and keeping safe techniques.

7. Ask each group to present their findings back to the rest of the young people and then facilitate a questions and answers session between groups, supplying answers if necessary.

The National Youth Agency

LEGAL DRUGS GAME

AIR FRESHENER	GLUE
MARKER PENS	LIGHTER FUEL
WINE	BEER
GIN	WHISKY
SILK CUT	PANAMA CIGARS
BENSON & HEDGES	ROLLUPS
PARACETAMOL	COUGH MIXTURE
ASTHMA INHALER	INSULIN
AEROSOL DEODERANT	WKD/BACARDI BREEZERS
RITALIN	VALIUM

20. POSTERS

This is a good activity for larger groups, but it will work if you have a smaller one by asking the young people to work in pairs.

Aim

To encourage the young people to research and share information about illegal drugs.

You will need

- Flipchart paper
- Glue
- Scissors
- Markers
- A wide selection of leaflets and information sheets about illegal drugs (try the FRANK website)
- Internet access (optional)

How to do it

Divide the main group into smaller groups of four. Put all of the information and leaflets you have collected about different drugs in a place that everyone can see and have easy access to.

Explain that you are going to designate each group the name of an illegal drug and that the group's task is to then research and design a poster to give information to other young people about it. The information should include:

- the legal classification of the drug;
- any street names they know;
- a description of the substance; and
- the effects it has on the body.

Explain that they can cut pictures out of the

leaflets, get information from the internet and use the markers to create their own images. Reinforce that this is not an anti-drugs poster you are asking them to create, but one that gives good, clear information that would be useful to young people to know.

Allow 30 to 40 minutes for the posters to be completed and then ask each group to present their poster and findings to the rest of the young people. Allow time for discussion and encourage questioning. Then review which poster the group thinks is the most effective and why. Put the posters to a show of hands vote.

Display the posters for other young people to see.

21. RISKS AND SKILLS

This group activity offers a scenario to work from. If you think that it is appropriate you can ask young people to work from their own experiences instead.

Aim
To identify risks and personal skills needed to make things safer.

You will need
- Flipchart paper and markers

How to do it
Ask the young people to imagine a train journey involving a group of young men and a group of young women coming home late after a night out. Both groups have had a top night out and are being quite loud, laughing and shouting.

At least two of the young women have drunk large amounts of alcohol and are feeling very sick and dizzy. The other young women have also been drinking but they are okay and are looking after their friends.

The young men, who the girls don't know, have been to a club and have all taken ecstasy, except for one young man who is sitting quietly slightly away from the larger group.

There is also an older woman in the carriage travelling alone and two older men seated together.

The young men notice the young women and start calling over to them to get their attention.

Now ask the young people to get into pairs and discuss what they think may happen next and the risks to safety they can identify to everyone involved.

Ask the young people to share in the large group some of their ideas. These could include risks such as one of the girls being sick on the train, arguments breaking out, getting off at the wrong stop or someone getting hurt. Draw out any behaviour that could be linked to the substances taken. For example the young men, who have used E, may not respect personal boundaries and get too close to the young women.

From the discussions pull out four main risks and write these on four sheets of flipchart paper.

Divide the young people into four groups and hand a 'risk' and some markers to each group to look at. Invite the young people to discuss the risk in their group and then record what could be done to reduce the risk to make it more likely that everyone in the carriage will get home safely.

Once they have done this ask them to look at the points they have made and think about what personal skills would be needed to be able to do this. For example, assertiveness or thinking ahead and phoning for help.

In the large group look at the skills

identified and facilitate a discussion. How many of the group feel confident that they have these skills? What do they think they would do in similar circumstances?

From this you can plan additional work to build on personal skills.

22. MEDIA WATCH

This activity can be expanded to looking at other forms of media such as movies or TV.

Aim

To review media articles about drugs misuse and promote discussion about the messages given.

You will need

- A good selection of newspaper/magazine articles
- Copies of the media watch sheet
- Pens

How to do it

Ask the young people to look through newspapers/magazines and cut out any articles that feature stories involving drugs.

Set a period of about two weeks for them to collect as much as they can, and collect as much as you can too so that there is a wide selection. Try and find the most diverse views that you can!

Divide the main group into smaller groups of four and invite them to share their articles, supplementing these with some you found. Allow about twenty minutes for discussion, encouraging the young people to record findings onto the Media Watch sheet.

Once everyone has finished invite the groups to share the 'messages'. Facilitate a whole group discussion to consider the drugs information given in the articles. Are the messages all the same? Which ones should be trusted? Is it different for celebrities and non-celebrities?

MEDIA WATCH SHEET

What it says	Newspaper/ magazine	Date	What message was being given

23. DRUGS CLASSIFICATIONS

Drugs are classified in many ways, for example; legal/illegal, prescription/non prescription, uppers/downers. This activity divides drugs into effects, although you need to stress to young people that these can vary from person to person dependent on where they are, who they are with and how they are feeling before they take them. It is also worth reinforcing the fact that a safe dose for one person could be dangerous, even fatal, for another.

Aim
To inform young people about the effects that drugs have on the body.

You will need
- Sets of the Drugs Classification sheet cut up and put into envelopes
- Three x A5 cards for each set marked 'STIMULANTS' 'DEPRESSANTS' and 'HALLUCINOGENS'

How to do it
Divide the young people into small groups of four or five.

Hand each group an envelope with the drugs slips inside and a set of the A5 cards. Explain that on the A5 cards are three categories that drugs tend to be split into based on the effects they have on the body when taken.

Each group's task is to discuss the drugs

on the cards and then place them in the category that they think fits the effect. Allow ten to fifteen minutes and then call time.

Go through the right answers asking the group to explain where they decided to place their cards and why. Tell the young people to award their group a point for each correct answer.

Reinforce what has been said and add up the points. The group with the most is the winner!

Uppers   Legal

Downers   prescription

illegal   Non prescription

STIMULANTS

Increase the activity of the central nervous system

DEPRESSANTS

Reduce the activity of the central nervous system

HALLUCINOGENS

Alter perceptions of reality and may result in hallucinations

DRUGS CLASSIFICATION CARDS

STIMULANTS	DEPRESSANTS	HALLUCINOGENS
Caffeine	Alcohol	Magic Mushrooms
Tobacco	Solvents	LSD
Methamphetamine	Minor tranquillisers	Cannabis
Amphetamines	Valium	Skunk
Ecstasy	Codeine	
Cocaine	Pethidine	
Crack	Heroin	
Poppers	DF118 (dihydrocodeine)	
Anabolic steroids	Morphine	
	Rohypnol	
	Opium	

Source www.talktofrank.com

24. DRUGS IN SPORT DEBATE

A news story is suggested for this activity. However, it is fine to substitute this for a local or more recent article.

Aim

This promotes discussion around decisions made following positive drug testing in sports.

You will need

- Copies of the news story
- Flipchart and markers

How to do it

Before you start open the session by explaining that the issue of drugs in sports is not a new one. In the 1960s Tommy Simpson, one of Britain's greatest cyclists, died during the Tour de France after taking a stimulant drug.

Go on to state that drugs are banned in sport to prevent one competitor gaining an unfair advantage over another. However, some athletes continue to take the risk despite knowing the consequences.

Now divide the young people into two groups and hand each group a copy of the news story. Set group one the task of formulating the argument for giving Alain Baxter his medal back. Tell group two that their task is to argue that the decision to strip Alain Baxter of his medal was the right one. Explain that each group will need to present their case to the other. Give out flipchart and paper for the young people to record points on.

Allow about twenty minutes for discussion and then set up the room for a debate with group one on one side and group two on the other.

Facilitate both sides of the discussion and then put the motion of giving Alain Baxter his medal back to the vote.

Pull out key points from the discussions and reinforce that there are 4,000 drugs banned by the International Olympic Committee (IOC) who set National Standards.

DRUGS IN SPORT NEWS STORY

Drugs at the 2002 Winter Olympics:

British skier Alain Baxter tested positive for methamphetamine in Salt Lake 2002, an addictive stimulant which affects the central nervous system.

Methamphetamine is a class B controlled drug and is a synthetic substance closely related to the stimulant drug amphetamine. Baxter was stripped of his Bronze Olympic medal, despite protesting that he was innocent of the charges.

Later it emerged that Alain had taken a banned drug by mistake (in a nasal inhaler). He was cleared of cheating and deliberate use of illegal pharmaceuticals.

"The ban's been lifted, they've accepted it was a genuine mistake, my name's been cleared and I can work from there." Alain said, "That's the most important thing."

His medal, that bronze acknowledgment of achievement, was not returned.

(Source; www.news.bbc.co.uk & www.sport. guardian.co.uk)

25. DRUGS IN SPORT

This activity gives specific information about drugs, their effects and the reasons why sportspeople may use them

Aim
To offer information about some of the drugs that are misused in sports.

You will need
- Copies of the drugs in sports sheet cut up
- Envelopes
- Drug leaflets

How to do it
Preparation
Before the session photocopy and enlarge the drugs in sports sheet. Then cut it up and place each set into an envelope after shuffling the drug name, effects and information cards. If you want to use the game again stick the cards onto A6 coloured card and laminate.

At the session
Before you start the game explain that when any drug is taken into the body (smoked, injected or swallowed) it goes into the bloodstream. As the blood is pumped into the brain the full effect of the drug is felt on the central nervous system, the system that controls how a person feels and acts.

Divide the main group up into threes or fours. Explain that the activity is basically a sorting game. You are going to hand each group an envelope that has within it cards with the name, effects and information about eight different drugs that are sometimes used by athletes illegally to improve their performance. The group's task is to 'sort' the cards so that they match the right name with the correct effect and information. Stress that it doesn't matter if they are unsure or get it wrong at this stage.

Allow fifteen to twenty minutes and then ask the groups to stop. Go through and tell the young people the correct card order and discuss as you go along.

Next hand out the leaflets to the groups and ask the young people to go through and find out one more thing about one of the drugs they have been looking at.

Once everyone has completed the second part of the task, bring the whole group back together and invite them to share the additional facts that they have learnt.

DRUGS IN SPORT

STIMULANTS	Gives the athlete a burst of energy, increases heart rate and brain activity.	Can be found in legal substances such as tea/coffee or cola and cold remedies as well as illegal drugs such as cocaine.
DIURETICS	Rids the body of excess water and can hide other illegal substances.	Sometimes misused by sportspeople to lose weight fast to keep under a specific weight to enter lower weight classes, for example boxers or jockeys.
HUMAN GROWTH HORMONE	Increases bone growth and helps the body to use energy more efficiently.	This causes other hormones that occur naturally in the body to be produced at an increased rate.
ANALGESICS	Painkillers such as Aspirin and morphine.	These may be used to mask pain, injury or illness so that athletes can continue to compete.

ANABOLIC STEROIDS	Helps build muscle bulk and increase ability to train for longer.	Women who use this have grown facial hair and developed deeper voices due to testosterone (the male hormone).
BETA BLOCKERS	Slows down the rate of breathing and heart rate.	These are only tested for in certain sports like archery, shooting and ski jumping because they would impair performance in endurance sports.
LOCAL ANAESTHETICS	This drug causes numbness in a part of the body. It is illegal when it is over a certain percentage in the bloodstream.	An athlete may use this drug to cover up or disguise an injury.

REVIEWING

26. DRUGS BAG

This review technique enables young people to share what they have learnt and identify gaps for further work.

Aim
To facilitate peer learning and identify areas that will need additional work.

You will need
- Post it notes
- Pens
- A small cloth drawstring bag

How to do it
Invite the young people to sit in a circle so that everyone can be seen and heard within the group. Hand everyone a Post it note and a pen and ask them to write a question in the middle of the paper about drugs that they know the answer to. For example "What class drug is Heroin?" or "Is Cocaine a stimulant or a depressant drug?" Once they have written something down, ask the young people to fold their paper and not show anyone else.

Then pass the bag around the circle and ask each group member to put his or her slip into it. When all the slips have been collected give the bag a good shake to mix the questions up. Stress that this game is not a chance to show off or make other members of the group feel stupid if they do not know the answer. It is an opportunity to learn from each other.

Now pass the bag around the circle, inviting

young people to take it in turns to take a slip out of it, answer if they can and then pass the bag on. If the young person doesn't know the answer, another member of the group can answer. If no one knows then the author of the question can answer. If there are any answers given that the group is not sure about or if anyone wants to challenge an answer then facilitate this. Agree with the group any areas that they feel they would like more information about for future sessions.

27. LEGAL REVIEW

Aim
To review knowledge about the legal classification of drugs under the Misuse of Drugs Act.

You will need
• A copy of the drugs circle enlarged
• A copy of the drugs sheet cut up

How to do it
Place the drugs circle in the middle of the group and remind the young people that drugs are classified under the Misuse of Drugs Act and some drugs, such as alcohol or tobacco, are controlled by other laws.

Give each young person a card with a drug on it and ask them to place it on the section of the drugs wheel that they think is correct. Stress that no one else can challenge where it is placed until everyone has had a turn.

Once the circle is complete ask if anyone wants to move a card and the reason why. Correct any incorrect cards (using the information in the Misuse of Drugs Act section) and review activity.

DRUG CARDS

HEROIN	ECSTASY	CANNABIS	COCAINE
CRACK	MAGIC MUSHROOMS	ROHYPNOL	SKUNK
GHB	VALIUM	AMPHETAMINES	BARBITURATES

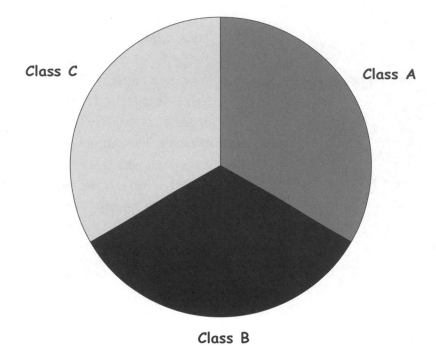

Class C

Class A

Class B

28. THREE THINGS
This is a quick activity to review learning.

Aim
To share knowledge and challenge misinformation

You will need
• Nothing

How to do it
Invite the young people to sit in a circle.

Then explain that each person is going to share three things about drugs that they know are correct. They will then share three things that they have heard about drugs that they now know to be untrue. For example 'Heroin is a Class A drug – true', 'Everyone who uses drugs becomes an addict – false'. Use the statements made as discussion points.

Move on to ask
• Where do we get our information around drugs from?
• How do we know it is right?
• Where can we check it out?
• Where can we go if we are concerned?

ADDITIONAL SUPPORT

Alcohol Concern
Alcohol Concern is the national agency on alcohol misuse. The site contains a range of information including fact sheets.
www.alcohol.concern.org.uk

ChildLine
Tel: 0800 1111 Freephone
Provides confidential help and counselling for young people.

Drugs Students Survival Guide
This site is aimed at students and gives information on drugs, drugs use, the law health and emergencies.
www.nistudentsdrugs.info/defaulttrue.asp

DrugScope
General information on alcohol and drugs and alcohol education.
www.drugscope.org.uk

D-World
DrugScope website for young people aged 11-14. Includes games, video diaries, quizzes and lots of information about drugs and their effects.
www.drugscope.org.uk/dworld

Jonny Long Life
Jonny Long Life provides information on issues for young people including sex, drugs and relationships.
www.jonnylonglife.com

Lifebytes
Health website aimed at 11 to 14-year-olds.
Includes information on alcohol, drugs and
mental health.
www.lifebytes.gov.uk

Mind Body and Soul
Website presents health information based
on the National Curriculum for Key Stage 4
(14-16).
www.mindbodysoul.gov.uk

Release
Legal advice on drugs
www.release.org.uk

Re-Solve
Re-Solve is the only national charity solely
dedicated to the prevention of solvent and
volatile substance abuse (VSA).
www.re-solv.org

Talk to Frank
Site mainly for young people but useful for
parents/carers too. Includes alphabetical
listing of drugs and their slang names. Also
an advice page.
www.talktofrank.com

Talk4Teens
Talk4Teens site has been developed through
the Durham Dales PCT Health Improvement
Team and ideas from young people in Wear
Valley and Teeside. Offers information on
health issues, including alcohol, drugs and
smoking.
www.talk4teens.co.uk

Urban 75

An e-zine for older teenagers with bulletin
boards, games, photos and a detailed section
on drugs, including a good first aid section.
www.urban75.com

Wotz da Factz

Information on a wide range of drug related
topics, including school exclusion and drug
using parents.
www.wotzdafactz.co.uk

Wrecked

An NHS/Health Promotion England website
for young people dedicated to alcohol issues.
www.wrecked.co.uk

***The National Youth Agency is not responsible
for the content of these websites.***

See also The National Youth Agency's online information toolkit for young people at www.youthinformation.com